The Traveller from The Heavens

Sr. Nafees Khan

Toronto, Canada

GOODWORD

www.goodwordbooks.com

Once the Prophet Muhammad ﷺ was seated with his companions.
A traveller in white came and asked several questions.

O, Messenger of Allah, "What is Iman?"
He ﷺ stated, "The basic belief is to believe in Allah
And in His most obedient creations, the Malaikah,

Iman is to believe in the Quran and all His scriptures
From Adam عليه السلام to Ahmad ﷺ, there were many messengers

Iman is believing that there will be an Akhira
When a day will come for us to meet our Creator."

Allah is One
Allah has no son
Allah has no partner
Allahu Akbar.

4

Angels are pure
Angels are light
Angels keep records
And always do right.

Quran is noble
Quran is universal
Quran is guidance
Quran is eternal.

6

Muhammadﷺ was Ummi
Muhammadﷺ is a model
Muhammadﷺ was last
Muhammadﷺ is the seal.

Akhira is Heaven
Akhira is Hell
Akhira is forever
Allah is the judge.

8

After the Prophet☪ had answered the question on Iman, The traveller was ready with the next one on Islam.

He☪ said, "Not committing shirk is part of our deen
Which is clearly written in Quran ul Hakeem

It is establishing the salah and paying the zakah
And fasting during the month of Ramadan

Islam is performing the Haj at least once if you can
And taking care in fulfilling all the Arkaan."

Salah is fard
Salah is a must
Salah washes sin
Salah is discipline.

Zakah is no tax
Zakah is no burden
Zakah is kindness
For those who need help.

Sawm is for Allah
Sawm is dear to Him
Sawm is training
Sawm is a blessing!

14

Haj is Tawaf
Haj is Sa'ee
Haj is Arafat
Haj is a duty.

The traveller then asked. "What is Ihsan?"
"It is worshipping as though you're seeing ar Rahman
If you cannot do that, then be sure that Allah can."

After that our Prophet was once again questioned,
"When will the Hour be that brings Dunya to the End?"

He replied, "I have no better knowledge than thee.
However, there are some signs that will be seen."

His companions were then informed that was Jibraeel
Who had come down to teach Islam, our Deen!

Ihsan is good
Ihsan is excellence
Ihsan is attainable
Ihsan must be our goal.

Jibraeel is an angel
Jibraeel is Nur
Jibraeel brought the Wahees
Jibraeel taught us deen.

Our life is deen
Our goal is deen
Islam is our deen
We are Muslims!

Note: This is based generally on a *hadith* that is
known as a Hadith Jibraeel. See the complete
Hadith in al-Bukhari, chapter 4 (Iman)

23

Glossary

Ahmad	another name for Prophet Muhammad
Akhira	The Last Day, Heareafter
Allahu Akbar	Allah is the greatest
Ar Rahman	the kind (Allah)
Arafat	a plain near Makkah/Mecca
Arkaan	essential parts of worship
Deen	faith, religion
Dunya	this world
Fard	compulsory
Hadith	the sayings/practice of the Prophet
Haj	pilgrimage (to Makkah)
His Scriptures	psalms of Dawud (David), Scrolls of Ibrahim (Abraham), Torah (revealed to Musa/Moses) Injeel (revealed to Isa/Jesus) peace be upon them all.
Hour	the Hour of Resurrection, Judgement Day, doomsday
Ihsan	perfection, better
Iman	faith
Jibraeel	archangel, chief angel
Malaikah	angels
Nur	light
Quran	a book revealed to Prophet Muhammad
Ramadan	month of fasting, 9th month of lunar calendar
Sa'ee	walking in between Mount Safa and Mount Marwa
Salah	prayers
Sawn	fasting
Shirk	believing in another god/s besides Allah, polytheism
Tawaf	circling the Kabah
Ummi	some one who could not read or write
Wahees	revelation, message from Allah
Zakah	charity

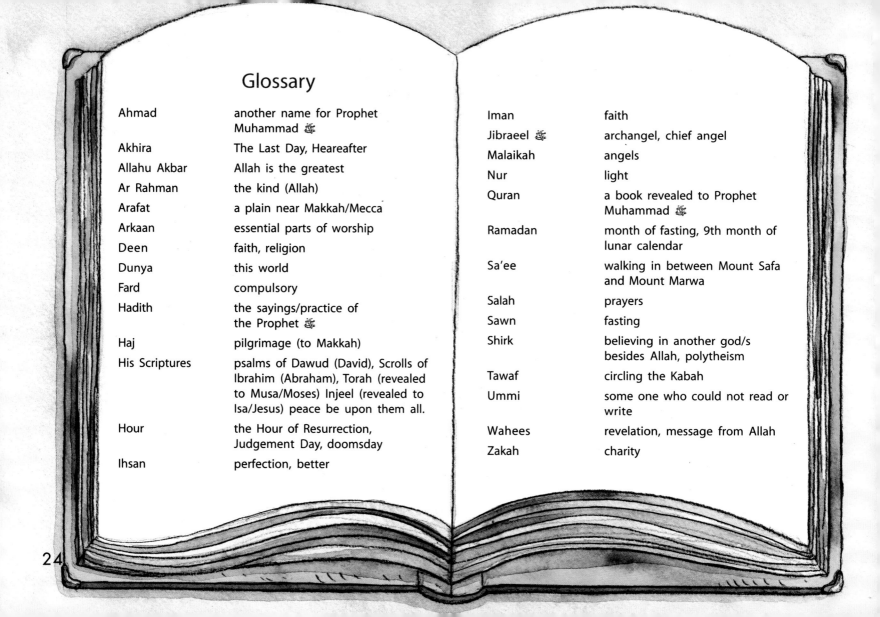